D0529367

The GOSPEL BLIMP

The
GOSPEL BLIMP

By JOSEPH BAYLY

Windward Press

HAVERTOWN · PENNSYLVANIA

THE GOSPEL BLIMP

Contents

The GOSPEL BLIMP

1

Conception of an Idea

THE IDEA really began that night several years ago when we were all sitting around in George and Ethel Griscom's backyard.

We'd just finished eating an outdoor picnic supper (a real spread), and there wasn't much to do except swat mosquitoes and watch the fireflies. Every so often an airplane flew over, high in the sky. You could see the twinkling red and white lights.

I guess that's what got us started on the Gospel Blimp. Or maybe it was George and Ethel's next-door neighbors, who were playing cards and drinking beer on the porch.

Anyway we began talking about how to reach people with the gospel. Herm's active in the local business-men's group (he and Marge were there that night, their first time out after the baby was born). So when we started talking about reaching people, Herm says, "Let's take those folks next door to you, George, for example. You can tell they're not Christians. Now if we wanted to give them the gospel, how'd we—"

"Herm, for goodness' sake, keep your voice down," Marge interrupted. "D'you want them to hear you?"

"Herm's right, they're not Christians," George agreed. "Go to church—a liberal one—Christmas and Easter. But drink and play cards most other Sundays. Except the summer. In a few weeks they'll start going to the shore each weekend until Labor Day."

"O.K. now. Any suggestions?" Herm is a good discussion leader.

"Hey, look at that plane. It's really low. You can almost see the lights in the windows."

"Portholes. More potato chips, anyone?"

"Like I was saying, here's a test. How do we go about giving the gospel to those people over there?" And Herm motioned toward the house next door.

"Too bad that plane didn't carry a sign. They looked up from their card playing long enough to have read it if it had carried one."

"Hey, you know you may have something there. Any of you seen those blimps with signs trailing on behind? You know, 'Drink Pepsi Cola,' or 'Chevrolet is First'?"

"Volkswagen sales are really increasing. I read the other day—"

"What I mean is this. Why not have a blimp with a Bible verse trailing—something like 'Believe on the Lord Jesus Christ and thou shalt be saved.'"

"I can see it now. The world's first vertical blimp, straight up and down like that tree. Anchored by a sign."

"Stop making fun. We could get a shorter verse."

"Sounds like a terrific idea. Really terrific. Why, everybody would get the gospel at the same time."

"Everybody except blind people and children who aren't able to read."

"Nothing's perfect. Anyway it does sound terrific, like Marge said."

"How'd we go about it? And wouldn't it be awfully expensive? I mean, buying the blimp, and blowing it up, and everything."

"Hey, it's time for the Maxie Belden show."

"Aw, who wants to watch TV on a night like this, stars and breeze and all. Well, if everybody else is going inside . . ."

I GUESS we'd have left it at that—just one of those crazy things you talk about when a group gets together for supper and the evening—if it hadn't been for Herm.

Like I said, Herm's a good organizer. (I mean, I said he's a good discussion leader. But he's a good organizer too.)

So the next Thursday Herm brought the idea up at our weekly businessmen's luncheon. He asked to make an announcement, and then he began. You could tell he was excited.

"Look, we want to reach people. And I've got a proposal to make. As you can see, we're not reaching them with our luncheons—" Here he paused and looked around the room. I did too, and I guess everybody else did. Not that we needed to. The regulars were there: three preachers and sixteen businessmen, two of them retired. And of course there was old Mr. Jensen. He doesn't do much any more, but he still owns about half the real estate around town. I mean, a lot of houses and buildings—not necessarily half. And all of them Christians—the men at the luncheon, that is.

Well, Herm summarized the Gospel Blimp idea. He really did a good job. You could just tell that different ones were getting excited as he talked. Nobody even started on their ice cream until he was through.

"And so I suggest," Herm ended, in a real loud voice, "that we appoint a committee. Maybe it's for the birds. Maybe not. But anyway," and here he paused and looked around the room again, "we ought to be reaching people somehow."

He'd hardly sat down when old Mr. Jensen was on his feet, real excited.

"Herm," he said, "I'm all for it. One hundred and ten per cent. 'Course, there'll be problems, but nothing ventured, nothing lost. I think you ought to be chairman of the committee, Herm. Young fellow like him has lots of spizzerinkum, Fred," he finished, with a wink at our president, Dr. Gottlieb.

That afternoon we were a little late ending the luncheon, but by the time we did a committee had been formed. With Herm as chairman.

"All you fellows on the committee, stay behind a few minutes," Herm called out above the scraping of the chairs as we rose to go. "We'll have to settle on a meeting time. This'll take work—lots of it."

2

Labor Pains

Lots of work. That was the understatement of the year—maybe of the century.

First off we found we'd have to incorporate, otherwise the businessmen's group would have been liable, or maybe us personally. Liable financially, that is.

That constitution was a bear. It took two trips to the state capital before we got it approved. But finally, there we were, "International Gospel Blimps, Inc." (We made it blimps instead of blimp because someone suggested the idea might spread. And if it did, we'd be in on the ground floor. Then Herm said, well, if it did spread, or if it might, why not be sure we take care of all eventualities. Why not make it "International" right from the start? So we did.)

Next we got stationery and receipts printed up. Since we'd gotten incorporated as a non-profit organization, we could include the line on the receipt about contributions being tax-deductible.

This took all our time, and I mean all our time, for

the next couple of months. That summer my lawn looked like a jungle. Especially after that week of rain late in the summer.

I remember that third week in August, because it was Friday evening and I had gone over to George Griscom's to decide on accounting procedures. Money had begun to come in and we'd just opened a bank account. It was about nine-thirty and we were coming along O.K. when someone knocked on the screen door.

George got up and went. I heard him thank whoever it was for mowing his lawn. Then they talked for a few more minutes and the man went away. I heard him call out, "Sorry you can't come," as he went off the porch.

"I'm sure glad you got that screen door closed," I said, half serious. "This place is crawling with mosquitoes."

"Listen," George says, and I can tell something's on his mind, "that was my next-door neighbor. Remember the guy who was drinking beer and playing cards with his wife on the porch when you were over in June? The night we dreamed up this Gospel Blimp idea? He just invited me, that is, Ethel and me, to go down to the shore with them this weekend. Of course I told him we couldn't go. Tomorrow's the full committee meeting, and Sunday afternoon's the I.G.B.I. prayer meeting.

"But that's not what I'm getting at," George continued. "What I mean is this. Wouldn't it be tremendous if he'd be the first fruit of the blimp? Both of them, I mean. It would sort of put a seal on it all if they'd become Christians. After all, they were why we thought of it in the first place."

So before I left Ethel came in, and the three of us had prayer together that their neighbors would be saved through the Gospel Blimp.

Somehow as I drove home through the darkness, there was a peaceful sense of rightness about the I.G.B.I. plan. Maybe I'd had it before, maybe not. But tonight I knew. This was for people. And people would be saved. People like the Griscoms' next-door neighbors.

I'VE SOMETIMES wondered whether we'd have started on the whole thing if we'd known at the very beginning all that was involved.

Not the money. I don't mean that. Like somebody once said (maybe it was that fellow who started missions in China), "Have faith, think big, and tell the people. You'll get the money." —And we did. It really came rolling in.

We were able to get an article about the Gospel Blimp in a Christian magazine, and did that ever stir up interest. We followed it up with a big advertisement. Money came in from all over. Also requests for information, suggestions of verses to be used at the blimp's tail, offers of hangar space, offers of uniforms for the crew. All kinds of offers.

At first I handled the correspondence, until I got swamped so bad I couldn't see my way out (complicated by its being Christmas and the kids having the measles). Honest, I never knew so many Christians were sign painters or had had experience on Navy blimps and ground crews. I answered 26 letters from sign painters and 19 from Navy blimp Christians (not counting about a hundred Air Force guys) before I gave up and handed the job over to Herm.

One old gentleman even wrote from Germany to say he'd be honored to give us technical advice. (Doc Gottlieb read it for me—it was in German.) Seems he'd served on the Hindenburg—missed its last trip because he'd fallen off a ladder the day before it left Frankfurt. He was willing to serve without compensation—only wanted his passage money across the Atlantic.

Like I said, the whole thing mushroomed like an inverted pyramid until we just had to do something. It was wrecking my home. I was out every night, and the only time I saw the kids was at breakfast. Love in our home meant "A bowl of cereal, a glass of milk, and you." (That's the year we celebrated Christmas five days late. At least the tree didn't cost us anything.)

So Herm finally decided to give up his job at the meat packing plant and go into the Gospel Blimp full-time. It was a big decision for him to make, giving up a good job with security and a pension and relatively safe work. On the other hand, as he pointed out to us, there was no real security in the Gospel Blimp, even though it looked promising. But he was willing to take a step of faith if we were behind him.

And we were. Especially me, for reasons that should be obvious. I was about at the end of my rope.

3

The Blimp Is Delivered

THE BLIMP was delivered in April. It drifted in, sort of lazy-like, from the East, where it had been manufactured.

We were all on hand, plus about five hundred other people, to see it come down into the hangar. (Did I tell you old Mr. Jensen gave some ground just beyond the city limits, down near the sewage disposal plant, for the hangar?)

It was a beauty. I've never seen Herm so touched—said it made him think of a perfect sausage, a perfect one.

That night we had a sort of send-off dinner up at Second Church. Speeches by the mayor (that was before the time when persecution began), by the head of the ministerial association (he too was extremely friendly still), and by a Christian Navy commander.

Afterward we all got in our cars and drove out to the hangar, where the Gospel Blimp was christened. Herm's little girl broke a bottle of Seven-Up over it. (We originally thought of Coke, but someone suggested that seven is the number of perfection, so we used Seven-Up.)

George Griscom invited us over to his house afterwards, everybody who'd been there that night we had the original idea for the blimp, almost a year ago. We were sort of sober, thinking of all that lay ahead.

"You know," George said, "if only my next-door neighbors are saved. If they are, it'll be worth-while. All the work and money and time."

"Listen," Herm said, "it can't fail. They can read, can't they? Well, tomorrow morning at eight sharp they'll see the gospel in the sky. Right over their house. I promise you, George, in my capacity as General Director of International Gospel Blimps, Incorporated. And not just your next-door neighbors. The whole block. My block. Every block in the city. Every last one. But we'll start with your block, George. Seems only right, doesn't it?" And he looked around the room for approval.

We all nodded or said yes, it sure did.

"What verse are you starting out with, Herm?"

"That would be telling. You'll see tomorrow morning, bright and early. Well, everybody, guess we'd better call it a night."

NEXT MORNING I drove past George's house on my way to work, starting a little early so I'd get there just at eight. Sure enough, there was the blimp. And trailing on behind was the sign. It was really beautiful, with the early morning sun highlighting those bold red letters.

Why, the gospel could be seen for blocks.

Maybe it was too early in the day, but I didn't see anyone out looking up at it. So after stopping the car for a minute across from George's house, I went on to work.

I went out for lunch that day (often I'd bring it in a bag, and just get a cup of coffee at the soda fountain on the first floor). But I went out, and first thing I did was look up between the buildings at the sky. No blimp.

So I walked several blocks to this little sandwich shop some of us go to, hoping I'd run into one or two of the fellows. Sure enough, George and a couple of others were there.

"Seen the blimp?" George asked me.

"First thing this morning, on my way to work."

"Boy, is it beautiful. You can see that sign almost a mile off."

"Wonder where it is now. Herm should have brought it downtown for the lunch hour."

"Well, there's going to be a lot of lunch hours before we're finished with that bag."

We didn't know it then, but we were almost finished with the blimp right at that moment. In fact, we found out later that's the reason Herm didn't have it downtown for the noon hour.

Seems Herm and the other guy (this graduate of a

Christian flying school we had hired) were cruising along just over the rooftops, when there was this tremendous jolt, followed by a hissing sound. Next thing they knew they were losing altitude, but fast.

Must have been a frightening experience. (Herm said later he expected the whole thing to go "thrrrp-p-p-*ssss,*" the way a balloon does when you blow it up and release it in the air without tying it, that is, the end you blow into. But it didn't.) In a few minutes they came to rest, sort of wedged between two houses.

I wish I'd been there to see those two women come running out of their front doors. One of them had been making beds upstairs when suddenly all the light from the outside was extinguished. So she ran over to the window, threw it open, and there was this thing. It sort of gave when she pushed against it, and there was this hissing sound. Well, she ran screaming into the street.

The other lady called the Fire Department, and they soon had a hook and ladder truck there.

"I've gotten cats out of trees, and kids out of bathrooms, but this is the first time I've gotten two guys off a blimp," this fireman in charge of the truck said, according to Herm. Herm says he used some other language, too, which was the opportunity for a witness.

It took a few weeks to get the blimp back in shape again. Seems they were flying too low, and the pilot wasn't watching carefully the way he should have been. Besides, he wasn't yet familiar with our little city. The big thing he didn't know was that a radio station's tower was located plumb in the middle of this residential section. So first thing he'd ripped the blimp's bottom on the tower. But finally it was ready to return to the air. (I mean the blimp. The radio station's programs weren't interrupted. That was no factor in the later persecution.)

4

Togetherness

MEANWHILE we'd gotten prepared for the long haul. By that I mean we learned a lesson from that first day. This job wouldn't be done overnight. There would be opposition; the enemy had already tried to ruin the blimp.

So we started prayer meetings for the safety of the blimp and those whose lives would be constantly endangered by flying in it. These prayer meetings were held downtown each noon hour for those of us who could come, in the International Gospel Blimps, Inc. office. (I forgot to tell you we'd rented three rooms in the Bender Building.) Thursdays we didn't meet there, since that was the day of the businessmen's lunch. But we spent a good bit of time in prayer at the lunch, too.

The wives had their prayer meeting every Tuesday night. They combined their praying with work on these fire bombs, which they filled.

But I'm getting ahead of my story.

After the rip in the blimp was repaired, Herm got the thing running on a regular schedule. This was possible because we let this other fellow, the first one we had, go. He was undependable, and besides he didn't know enough about flying, as witness the radio tower episode. But we really got a wonderful replacement who had spent four years flying Navy blimps out of Lakehurst, New Jersey. He was a young married fellow who'd been considering the mission field. In fact, he'd applied for South America or Africa or someplace. But, with his wife's help, we finally convinced him that this was much more strategic, because look at all the kids and young people he could influence for missions with this job.

Just so I won't forget this part of the blimp's ministry, let me tell you that this new fellow wasn't with us very long before he convinced the board that we should have a missionary emphasis on the blimp. So we decided that every Saturday afternoon would be Missionary Blimp Afternoon. (We chose Saturday because we knew the Christian kids don't go to the movies then, like so many other kids.) We used missionary signs on the blimp and released junior missionary bombs.

I was interested to see how my own kids would be affected by this new missionary emphasis, especially because they'd sort of come to resent the time I (also their Mother) was spending on blimp work. Maybe resent is too strong a word. It was more a matter of their saying, "Aw, another night out working on the blimp? You haven't been home since a week ago Saturday." They also were rather bitter about what happened at the football game.

Anyway, I was really happy when this one Sunday on the way home from church my boy brought up the subject. He said he'd been thinking about the blimp, and the missionary sign the blimp had pulled the afternoon before (it was, I believe, the ONE BILLION UNREACHED one).

As a result of all this thinking, he said, "I've decided to learn to pilot a blimp when I grow up. I'm going to enlist in the Navy."

"It's not fair," says his little sister. "It's really not fair at all. Boys get to do everything. I could never be a missionary. Girls don't get to learn to fly blimps. All they get to do is play with dolls and wash the bathroom floor and—" She stopped for breath.

"Huh," says our oldest girl, the one who's in high school, "who'd want to have anything to do with a blimp anyway? Only a creep. A real square creep. Brother, I mean, that Gospel Blimp is—"

"Judy, be careful of your mouth," her mother warns her. "It can get you in trouble."

"Trouble? What do you call what I and the other Christian kids got in over what happened at the game with Central? I guess the blimp had nothing to do with *that*. My mouth didn't get us into that trouble. There we were, ahead at the half, and then that darn blimp has to come along and—"

"Judy, that will be enough. You may set the table when we get home."

"Besides," I felt constrained to add in the blimp's defense, "everyone agrees that it was one of those freak accidents. One chance in a million of its happening. You can't really blame the blimp."

I THINK I told you about the fire bombs we were using. We named them that because they represented revival fire falling on the unsaved.

The I.G.B.I. Women's Auxiliary fixed them, like I said, at their weekly meetings. Wasn't really much to making them—they just took a tract and wrapped it up in different colored cellophane. There were loose ends sticking out, so that when they were dumped overboard from the blimp, they sort of floated to earth.

At first the kids chased them all over—I hear someone spread the rumor that there was bubble gum in them. But after a couple of days no one got particularly excited when they fell.

The Commander (Herm wanted us to call him that now) made quite an affair out of dumping the load, according to the blimp pilot.

"Bombs away!" he'd shout, and then he'd shoot them down, alternating colors (each color was a different tract).

And always, when he'd have a new tract, he'd try to dump some on George Griscom's next-door neighbor's lawn. He wasn't forgetting, the Commander wasn't, our covenant with George about his neighbor.

Not that there was any encouragement along that line.

Once, I recall, I stopped at Griscoms' to return George's power drill. I'd been getting the P.A. system ready to install on the blimp. So I asked Ethel about their neighbors.

"Nothing new," she says. "I mean, nothing to get excited about as far as their salvation is concerned. But she hasn't been well. I think they took her to the hospital two or three days ago. We can see him eating over there alone at night. And always a bottle of beer. Sometimes two."

"What hospital's she in?" I asked.

"I don't know. I'll tell George you stopped with the drill. By the way, how's the sound system coming?"

"Oh, some bugs yet. But give us a few more nights like tonight and we'll be ready to roll."

"Will people really be able to hear it?"

"With a hundred watts output? And three cone speakers? Listen, they'll be able to hear it anywhere— even in a basement. No worry about that."

"The Women's Auxiliary is really thrilled about the sound system. You know, we've been concerned about blind people, and children who can't read yet, and people who are near-sighted. And people who can't get outside to see the blimp, like invalids, and old men and women in convalescent homes, and people in hospitals. It'll be comforting to know we're doing something for them."

"Well, tell George I stopped. And thanks for the drill."

5

A Small Cloud

WHEN WE STARTED using the P.A. system about a week later, a new epoch in the Gospel Blimp's ministry began. In a sense, it seemed to give final assurance that the total evangelization of our little city was a distinct possibility.

But it also marked the beginning of the period of active opposition. Forces were unleashed which we hardly knew existed beneath the calm surface of life all around us.

I'll never forget that first night. I had gone down to the drugstore to get a box of candy and a card (having been reminded during dessert that it was our wedding anniversary), when suddenly I heard it.

In loud tones, on the wings of the night as it were, came the sound of "Rolled away, rolled away, rolled away, every burden of my heart rolled away." Honest, it was tremendous.

People came out of houses, cars stopped, everybody tried to figure where it was coming from.

Of course I knew. For I had put the last Phillips screw through the third speaker only that afternoon.

But the rest of the people were puzzled because the blimp was nowhere in sight.

Next came a vibraharp rendition of the Glory Song, followed by about fifty kids singing the Hash Chorus. But it wasn't until the music had stopped and the Commander's voice came on, "Now hear this, all you people," that the blimp hove in sight. It wasn't full moon, but it was still bright enough to see the blimp clearly outlined against the sky.

I suppose the Commander preached about ten minutes first time. Or maybe it took ten minutes for the blimp to get out of earshot. But even though it was short, he was able to get in two invitations. The vibraharp came on for a few bars of "Almost Persuaded" each time. (I should explain that the music was recorded on tape, although Herm's messages were live. It was only later that he taped the full program, including his own preaching. But that was while he was out of town.)

I tell you, I was really thrilled. When I got home with the candy, I phoned up Griscoms to tell them the good news.

"I know why you're calling," says George before I have a chance to tell him. "Listen." And he holds the phone away from his head. In the background, coming through clear as a bell, I can hear, "Hallelu, Hallelu, Hallelu."

Were we ever enthused. I think, looking back, that night was the high point of the whole blimp project. But we were totally unprepared for the next morning.

I picked up the *Trib* on my way to the office. And there on the front page, down toward the bottom, was a story about the "air-borne sound truck." It was the first time the blimp had hit the papers. (Earlier there had been a few lines about the christening, and a notice of the public meeting, but nothing like this.)

I guess I must have been sort of walking on air when I came into the office. Of course the guys I work with had known for a long time about my interest in the blimp. But they had sort of treated it something like— well, like the guy who bowls every night, or the fellow who's a scoutmaster. So now they could see the significance of my project, and they had probably even heard the gospel the night before.

Anyway, I sort of remarked casual-like after I'd hung up my coat, "You fellows see the newspaper story on the blimp?"

"Which one?"

"Why, there is only one," I say. "You know, the one I'm interested in, the gospel one."

"No, I mean which story? There are two, or didn't you know?"

"Where's the other one? I only saw the one on the front page." And suddenly I'm sort of sorry I brought up the subject, because everybody's quiet and nobody's smiling.

"Well, then, maybe you'd better read the one on the editorial page, Buster."

So I sat down at my desk and read it. It was an editorial entitled "The Right to Peace." And it began—

here, I have a copy—"For some weeks now our metropolis has been treated to the spectacle of a blimp with an advertising sign attached at the rear. This sign does not plug cigarettes, or a bottled beverage, but the religious beliefs of a particular group in our midst. The people of our city are notably broad-minded, and they have good-naturedly submitted to this attempt to proselyte. But last night a new refinement (some would say debasement) was introduced. We refer, of course, to the air-borne sound truck, that invader of our privacy, that raucous destroyer of communal peace. That the voices of some of our city's beloved school children were used does not take away from . . ."

Well, that's enough for you to get the general drift.

It seemed as if lunch would never come. When it did, I hurried over to the place I mentioned before, even though I'd brought my lunch. I mean the lunchroom where the Christian fellows often eat.

As soon as I saw them I knew we'd all had the same experience.

We talked it over, including all the angles. And when it came time for us to get back to work, someone —maybe it was George—seemed to sum it up when he said, "Well, we were told we'd be persecuted for righteousness' sake, and I guess this is it. So we'll just have to stand together, four-square."

THAT NIGHT our I.G.B.I. Board of Directors held an emergency meeting downtown to discuss the situation.

We'd hardly gotten started when the phone rang. It was the pilot—he'd just returned from supper to take the blimp out for its final run of the day. When he got inside the hangar, he found someone had broken in and sabotaged the blimp's P.A. system. Nothing else was touched.

The Commander told him to lock up and go on home for the night, and not to talk to anybody about what had happened. Then we settled down to discuss what to do. Somehow it seemed a much more pressing matter than it had before the phone call.

When we broke up around midnight, we'd come to certain decisions. In the first place, we decided that we'd continue to use the P.A. system on the blimp, no matter what happened. But we'd tune down the volume a bit. Next, we'd see if we couldn't get the sign electrified so that people could see where the sound was coming from when we broadcast at night. And finally, on the Commander's recommendation, we decided to hire a public relations man who'd be responsible for keeping the blimp in good with the general public. The Commander also said such a man could get money from Christians to pay for the blimp and the salaries and the sound system and the office and everything else.

The whole operation was costing about five thousand dollars per month, and even with contributions coming in from all over the country, it was still a strain. So we gladly voted to accept Herm's recommendation. I might even say that we breathed a sigh of relief. At least I did, because we were in a whole lot deeper than we ever imagined we'd be that Thursday afternoon about ten months ago when Herm first brought the blimp up at our businessmen's lunch.

6
Architect of Good Will

THAT NEW public relations fellow really knew his business. First thing he did was arrange a big dinner—to recoup our forces and make new friends, he said. The I.G.B.I. Women's Auxiliary worked on it and it was really well planned. Ham and sweets and everything else, with ice cream blimp molds for dessert. For favors they had little blimp banks—to save up money so you could pay your pledge, that is, if you made one. The whole dinner was gratis—there were no tickets and no offering. Just the opportunity to pledge at the end.

It was a bit disappointing that some of the people we invited didn't come. The mayor declined because of a previous engagement, and he was also too busy to write us a letter to be read at the dinner.

But the dinner was just the beginning of this public relations fellow's activity. As he expressed it, "Any item of interest about the blimp or its ministry is legitimate news. And news builds good will."

So he got little items in the papers about how much helium the blimp contained and where the helium

36   THE GOSPEL BLIMP

came from, about the Commander moving to his new
house, about the church affiliations of members of the
board, about the Women's Auxiliary luncheons and
parties, about the electric generating plant on the blimp,
about all sorts of other things. One or two of these
items even made the radio news summary.

He also had a regular news service for Christian
magazines, with plenty of photographs. Pictures of the
Commander releasing the millionth fire bomb were
published by about ten different periodicals. Another
time a picture of the Commander at the wheel made
the front cover of a big Christian magazine.

This public relations fellow was working on the
theory that International Gospel Blimps, Inc., was too
impersonal. People couldn't feel "empathy," as he put
it, with a non-profit corporation, or even with a blimp.
Too big and fat and cold. So more and more he built
up the Commander as the blimp's personification. He
got the Commander to grow a beard (like the guys in
those magazine advertisements), and also to wear a
new uniform. The old one was something like a police-
man's, but the new one was beautiful. Powder blue,
with shiny gold buttons and gold stripes on the sleeves.
That visor had enough braid on it for an admiral.

The Commander was spending less and less time
on the blimp. At our new public relations man's suggestion he joined the best golf club, so he could meet
the people whose influence really counts, and who
could contribute substantially to I.G.B.I. He also began taking speaking engagements all over—not just

churches, but service clubs and women's clubs and other meetings of that sort.

That summer he wasn't around much, because he had a full schedule of engagements at Bible conferences. Sometimes he took Marge with him, but mostly he'd just go off in his Mercedes Benz alone.

I'm told he had quite a ministry at these conferences, especially in terms of getting young people to dedicate their lives to Christian service. He talked a lot about sacrifice, and told about how he'd given up a successful career in business when he felt the call. No holding back, no looking around from the plow. Straight ahead, whatever the cost.

And the money really came in. There was no doubt about that public relations fellow knowing what he was doing.

Funny thing happened about this time. The Commander was leaving on one of his trips this particular Thursday afternoon, and he came to the businessmen's luncheon first. He wasn't able to come very often any more, so we were all glad to see him.

Herm gave a report, and then we reminisced some, recalling how enthusiastic old Mr. Jensen (the one who gave us the land on which the hangar was placed) had been that first time we ever discussed the blimp. Most of us had been at Mr. Jensen's funeral a few weeks before. (Incidentally he left $5,000 in his will to I.G.B.I., some to the Commander too, in view of his sacrifice.)

Anyway, after the meeting, while Herm was talking

to different men, some of us fellows decided to play a little joke on him. So we got a bushel of fire bombs and dumped them in his car.

A few minutes later, when Herm got in the driver's seat, we told him we'd loaded the bombs for him to drop on his trip. As far as we were concerned, it was just a practical joke. We were all standing around ready to empty the bombs back into the basket and take them away.

But Herm didn't take it as a joke. He sort of froze, didn't even say goodbye, and drove off. Later we found them dumped on the ground out near the hangar.

7

Cloudburst

THAT FALL everything was going fine, and all of us had sort of settled down to the kind of life we'd known before the blimp came along.

The blimp was on a regular schedule, flying all over the city during the daytime, concentrating on shopping centers and special events at night. People had come to accept the blimp—fact is, there was a sort of community pride of ownership. No other place had a Gospel Blimp, you know, although a lot of them had expressed interest.

Opposition to the blimp had all but died out, largely as a result of turning down the volume on the P.A. system and the public relations work.

There was one new development: foreign language programs. Although they weren't large, our city had several foreign sections. These included Chinatown, Italian and Polish communities, and one suburb that was largely German. So we rigged up signs in these languages and also recorded foreign language programs on tape. Then we had regular days and nights during the month when the blimp concentrated on each of these foreign groups.

It was one of these nights, the Polish one, when all the good will Herm and the public relations fellow had been building up came crashing around us. And not just the non-Christians; Christians were screaming for our hides just as loudly.

That Tuesday evening began in our home about the same as it did in thousands of other homes, I guess. We'd finished supper and the kids were hurrying to get the dishes done so they wouldn't miss any of the television programs. Tuesday night was, of course, the best night on TV. That was our downfall.

Let me explain at this point that the Gospel Blimp took to the air about seven o'clock that night. Everything was shipshape: the Polish sign was already lighted up, the baskets were full of fire bombs, the tape recorder was loaded and ready to roll with a completely Polish program. Everything was shipshape with one exception. But we couldn't have known ahead of time about that one particular thing. Even the Federal Communications Commission later admitted that at the public hearing.

At any rate, we had just settled down in front of the TV set to watch "Pistol Bark" when the sound sort of fades and instead of hearing what's happening on the program, we're listening to some sort of foreign gibberish.

"Hey, what's happening?" I ask. "Turn it to some

other channel and let's see if it's just on the one station."

One station, every station: the same foreign language program.

"Boy, is some radio station going to get it in the neck for this blooper," I say.

And then it happens. The speaking ends and a vibra-harp rendition of "Sunshine, sunshine, in my soul today" begins. Four verses.

A guy gets pumped full of lead, lips move, a horse gallops away. But no sound. Just "Sunshine, sunshine, in my soul today."

The program ends, and little cigarettes march around on the screen, out of step, to the tune of "Sunshine, sunshine, in my soul today."

By this time I'm on the phone, and so are fifty thousand other people. I wait and wait for the dial tone, finally give up.

Besides, what can I do? What can anyone do?

Next comes the Maxie Belden show, the most popular program on TV—or at least it was then. Maxie comes on with a great big smile and begins talking Polish. This girl with the low-cut dress sings, only her voice is bass, and the words are "Dwelling in Beulah Land." In Polish. It was horrible. I can't describe how I felt.

My oldest girl, the one in high school, begins to cry.

"What's the matter?" I ask. "Don't take it so hard. You can see what's going on even if you can't hear it."

"It's not that," she sobs. And then she lets out a real

wail: "What am I going to say tomorrow at school? This is awful—much awfuller than what happened at the game with Central. Oh, that darn, horrible blimp." And she runs upstairs to her room.

"Maybe," I suggest, but without much conviction, "maybe it's not on all the TV sets. Maybe ours is an exception."

But just a few seconds later any lingering, hopeful doubts were dissipated by the sign. It was printed rather crudely, I guess by the local station engineer: "Due to circumstances beyond our control, interference prevents listeners in this area from receiving sound on this or any other channel. Steps are being taken to correct this situation. Meanwhile keep tuned to this station."

Just then the phone rings. George Griscom is really upset. He'd been trying to get hold of the Commander but he's out of town. Marge doesn't know where he is, except that he left early this afternoon.

"What are we going to do?" George practically shouts over the phone. "Every minute that goes by, our stock gets lower with people. Maybe they'll even tar and feather us—I wouldn't put it past them. Not when you interfere with the Maxie Belden show."

"Nothing we can do," I admit. "After all, there's no telephone connection to the blimp. Let's see, it's about eight-thirty now. He's due to stay up there another two hours, maybe longer on a clear night like this."

"What in the world's causing it? The TV interference, I mean."

"I'm not sure, but somehow or other the blimp's

amplifier is broadcasting on television frequency. It shouldn't really be transmitting at all, but it is. And it's a freak that the picture is O.K. I'd expect it to go with the sound."

"Maybe we could build a big fire or something," George suggests in a hopeless sort of any-port-in-a-storm tone of voice.

"How'd he know we meant him? And how'd we get him to bring the blimp down?"

Every television station in town had the same idea, though. Before long we heard guns and rockets going off. But who up in a blimp is going to think they're trying to attract *his* attention? It's just a big celebration in town that he didn't know about. Maybe, since it seems to be mainly localized beneath him, it's a Polish holiday.

And even when some private planes begin to buzz the blimp, it doesn't mean anything to him. Just crazy pilots, having some sort of drag race, using the blimp as their turning mark.

The one man who could have changed the situation in a moment was the one man who was totally unaware that anything was happening. Just the flip of a switch and peace would have flooded the community. But he didn't know. And so for two more hours the switch was left unflipped. Vibraharp, ten minute sermon, invitation, "Almost Persuaded," hymn or chorus, vibraharp, on and on, around and around. Everything in Polish except the vibraharp.

And it came out here, on TV. Every channel, every set.

Some people called it a night and went to bed about nine-thirty, we found out later. They were in the happiest frame of mind, relatively speaking, next day.

Like I said earlier, it was a clear night. So the pilot kept going until about ten to eleven. Then he turned off the lights and the P.A. system and headed back to the hangar, blissfully unaware of what awaited him there.

He said later that he wondered why the big crowd. But he sure found out soon enough after he'd maneuvered the blimp into the hangar.

First were the police, with a summons for disturbing the peace. Then the reporters and photographers. And everywhere the crowd of people, raving mad, some of them shouting, "Let us have the bum! Burn the blimp!"

And in the background, waiting around until the police dispersed the crowd, were the board members of International Gospel Blimps, Inc.

Somehow or other, I think all of us realized that night was the beginning of the end. The end of the blimp as we had known it, the Gospel Blimp, which had come into our lives and filled them and crowded out almost everything else.

The wonderful, shiny blimp. The "darn" blimp, to use my oldest girl's usual description. The blimp that had its origin almost two years ago, that summer evening in George Griscom's backyard.

I look over at George, sitting on a box by the fence,

waiting. Good old George, so faithful all these months to the blimp and its ministry. George and Ethel, so anxious for their next-door neighbors to be saved through the Gospel Blimp. Here the end is in sight and they're not yet saved. All that praying for them, and they're not saved. All those special trips the blimp has made, flying low over their house, P.A. blaring away, fire bombs dropping. And they're not yet Christians. No wonder George looks so discouraged, sitting over there.

It seems forever, but finally the police get the crowd cleared away from the hangar and the people begin to get in their cars. A little group has found a basket of fire bombs, and they're standing around the fire it makes in the middle of the field. But even that group is beginning to joke, and seems to be getting in a better mood. For one thing, the pilot's reaction was so honest when he found out what's happened that the crowd had to laugh.

"Think we'll post a couple of men here for the night, just in case," the police lieutenant says to the pilot. "Never can tell.—Not that I'd mind, particularly. Not after what happened to the Maxie Belden show and getting that emergency call out here when I was all comfortable at home. But duty's duty.—Want an officer to drive home with you, also just in case?"

"No," says the pilot. "I've got to see some friends first anyway—the Gospel Blimp board members. That's them over there. I guess we'll have a lot of talking to do."

"Well, call your precinct if you need us during the night. Think I'll get on home to the late-late show.— And by the way, I think I'd keep that thing in the hangar the next few days."

"Thanks for the advice. Also for the help earlier. I thought for a while they might be thinking about lynching me, or at least they'd throw me in the sedimentation pool at the sewage disposal plant over there."

"You were lucky, my friend. But don't push it. 'Night." And the lieutenant swung into the police car.

"Hi, fellows," the pilot says to us as we close in on him. "Where's Herm? Where'll we go to talk? I want to sit down, wherever it is. I don't know about you guys, but I've just had a tough two hours. For awhile there I was wishing I was out on the mission field."

"We," George says firmly, with emphasis, "we've had a tough *five* hours. Almost six."

"Well, don't blame it on me," says the pilot. "I was only the pilot. I never claimed to be an electric engineer. Besides, it was me almost got tossed in with the sewage. Let's get away from here. This place gives me the creeps."

So we went over to George's place. Ethel fixed coffee and egg sandwiches for us. We didn't stay long though —only about an hour. There wasn't much we could decide, what with Herm not being there and all.

But we did have some prayer about the situation before breaking up. And we remembered to pray for George and Ethel's next-door neighbors. Ethel suggested that we should.

8

Truth Is Organized

ERM GOT BACK next day around noon. First thing he did after finding he'd backed into a hornet's nest was get together with the public relations fellow.

What they came up with wasn't what the rest of us expected, but you could see that it was only reasonable. Or at least we came to see that it was after they explained it to us. Our first reaction on seeing the evening newspapers, I'll admit, wasn't good.

What they did was this. The public relations man drew up a statement which Herm signed, and copies were taken to all the papers and radio and television stations.

In this statement Herm first apologized to the public for the inconvenience caused by the "irresponsible actions" of International Gospel Blimps, Inc. He next expressed regret that he had been out of town on business the previous evening, when these irresponsible actions had come to such an unfortunate climax. Then he said how if he had been here it would never have happened. (I never could understand that part of his statement. After all, Herm knows nothing about electronics.) But now that he was back again, he promised the public that he personally would see to it that there would be no repetition of the previous night's "fiasco." And, further, he wanted to assure our city that he would see to it that "any irresponsible element" in I.G.B.I. was dropped, and that this great community project would have "increasing civic consciousness." Finally, he appealed to the public for their sympathetic understanding of the tremendous pressures under which he had been working.

Well, that's about what Herm's statement said.

That night the board met in special emergency session. All of us had read the statement in the papers or heard it over television or radio. So we were sort of quiet when we came together down at I.G.B.I. headquarters.

"Hi, fellows," Herm says when he comes in with the public relations fellow about a half hour late. "What's everyone so solemn for? You'd think you'd lost your best friend or something. Cheer up, everything's settled. We've got it made. Haven't we?" he asks, turning to the public relations fellow.

"Sure have, Commander," he replies.

I guess this was too much for George Griscom. So he begins, "About that statement you gave to the papers, Herm—"

"Oh, that. Just to quiet people down. Really nothing to it, nothing more than that. You know how it is. We've been in this thing from the beginning and we've weathered a lot of storms together. Good ship. Good fellowship. Nothing to it."

"Commander, could I put in a word?" asks the public relations fellow.

"Sure thing. Only hurry—I want to get this meeting over with. Big day tomorrow."

"I'd like to explain why we issued that statement. You see, like I've told you before, it's hard to sell an idea. It's easier to sell a man. It's hard to sell a corporation, non-profit or regular. It's much easier to sell an individual—especially a guy like the Commander. You all know that.

"Well, once you've sold people on somebody as representing the idea or the movement," he continues, "you have to see that they never lose confidence in him. They can lose confidence in the idea, they can lose confidence in the corporation. With all due respect to you men, they can even lose confidence in the members of the board.

"But there's one person," he concludes, pointing his finger at us, "they can't lose confidence in. That's the man you've built up as a symbol. In the case of I.G.B.I. that's the Commander."

Everything's quiet for a minute or two. Then George Griscom asks, only he's not really asking, "So you decide to sell the rest of us down the river."

"Of course not," Herm interrupts before the public relations fellow has a chance to reply. "Of course not. That's not fair, George, if you don't mind my saying so. All it amounts to is this. Which is more important:

you or the blimp? If you had to choose, which would it be: your membership on the board, or the success of this Gospel Blimp project? After all, George, you must remember that you have a great deal more at stake than many others. It's *your* next-door neighbors we've given special attention to. I've asked for no special thanks from you for all I've done. Fact is, I've sacrificed a great deal without much appreciation. But then when something like this comes along, you can hardly blame me for wanting to see just a bit of loyalty from you fellows."

George sort of has a hang-dog expression.

"Actually it was a godsend that the Commander was out of town last night during the television incident," the public relations man continues. "If he'd been here, everybody would have known that he could do no more than anyone else to correct the situation. And the net result would have been a loss of public confidence in him. That would have been disastrous. A man in his position, like I said, may have feet of clay, but we've got to hide them from the public.

"The question isn't whether the Commander could or couldn't have done anything about the mess if he'd been here at the time it happened. It's that we can't let people *know* he couldn't. We've got to preserve their image of the Commander as a man who is in complete control of every situation."

"Would you lie to do that?" George says it real soft.

"That's a nasty word," the Commander says, looking straight at George. "And it's hardly a Christian attitude toward someone who's done as much for the Gospel Blimp as he has," putting his arm around the public relations fellow's shoulder.

"I guess there isn't much more to discuss, is there?" someone remarks, standing up.

"Just this," the Commander says. "Sit down a minute. Any of you guys don't like the way I'm running things, then, if you don't, why, for the sake of our harmony and testimony as a Christian organization, I think you ought to drop off the board. Nobody is indispensable."

"Except Herm," George murmurs close by my ear. "Nobody but Herm."

That was the last board meeting George ever attended. He just sort of dropped out. It made us all feel bad, but after all, there was a lot to be done. And personal feelings had to be subordinated to the Gospel Blimp. This was no time for discord. It was a time for pitching in, for rolling up our sleeves, for putting our heads to the grindstone.

THE BLIMP WEATHERED the storm with only one casualty: the P.A. system. We had to agree to drop that in order to satisfy the F.C.C., the City Council and public opinion. Also most of the Christians. Nobody wanted a repeat of the Maxie Belden incident.

So we settled down to the long haul. None of us on the I.G.B.I. board had quite the same feelings as we'd had earlier. But we decided that we'd put these things out of our mind for the blimp's sake.

Same way with Herm's family trouble. When we heard that he wasn't living at home any longer, and why he'd been taking those trips out of town, that really knocked us for a loop, temporarily. But after discussing it a long time (the meeting didn't end until three A.M.), with Herm not in on the discussion, we decided to give him the benefit of the doubt. Besides, as somebody said, Herm has really given himself to this project, right from the very start. Who else would have had the faith to take such a step as giving up his job at the meat packing plant?

After Marge actually filed for divorce, the issue became a lot bigger. For awhile I thought it would split the board, but we were able to hold things together for the sake of the blimp. Our only loss was the blimp's pilot—he resigned, after trying to get the board to do something about Herm. But there were plenty of Christian pilots around, and we got a good one.

As for Herm, he was spending more and more time in public relations work. By now he was in good with most of the civic and business leaders of our city. This brought in a fair amount of income, including grants from several foundations. (But it was still the thousands of little people, Christians, whose regular gifts paid the bills.)

9

Autumn Flight

ONE PLACE that Herm cultivated these important people was at the country club. He liked to play golf and these executives seemed to like having him around.

The issue that really threatened to split our I.G.B.I. board began, innocently enough, on the golf course.

Herm had given orders to the blimp pilot that he wasn't to fly over the country club. The distraction bothered people who were playing, Herm said, and besides, since he—the Commander—was there so much, the blimp really wasn't needed. And of course the pilot obeyed his instructions.

This one day, though, the pilot must have forgotten. Or maybe, since it was a beautiful fall afternoon, he just decided to go for a drive in the country.

At any rate, the blimp drifted over the golf course, its sign trailing along behind. Herm and three other fellows were playing the ninth hole. (He gave us all this background information at the next board meeting.) Besides Herm, the group included the president of Dunlevy-Sanders advertising agency, the Chamber of Commerce executive director, and the treasurer of National Steel.

"Say," one of them said, "that's your blimp, isn't it, Herm?"

"Yes, it is. You're next, I believe."

"Looks beautiful up there. Wonderful idea. Every eye can see it. Outstanding example of institutional advertising."

"Yes," somebody agreed (I think Herm said it was the head of Dunlevy-Sanders). "It's remarkable one other way, too. Almost any of the advertising media is limited to a particular class or income group. You choose the *Post* and you reach the broad middle class. *Fortune* or the *Wall Street Journal* gets you a different group—quite selective. But that blimp up there—well, you can see that it gets through to us just as easily as it does to the day laborer."

"Ever think of broadening its appeal?" asks the Chamber of Commerce man.

"What do you mean?" Herm is interested.

Fortunately they were the only ones on the course that afternoon, and nobody was pushing to play through. So they just stood there at the ninth hole talking and looking up at the Gospel Blimp. You have to see it to realize how beautiful that blimp is against a brilliant blue sky when the leaves are turning. Of course, the same thing is true at other seasons of the year, but I always thought it looked best in the fall.

"I mean that your blimp is sort of limited to a religious message. Now if you'd just broaden it a bit, the impact would be tremendous. Real piggy-back advertising value."

"I get your point," says the Dunlevy-Sanders president. "Just like those institutional ads by Continental Can—those classic 'Great Ideas of Western Man' ads."

"Right. Only in this case it would be a much closer relationship. I mean, what connection do tin cans or plastic bags have with Western civilization? But Christianity and Western civilization have grown up together. They're a natural. Pair them up and it does them both good. Piggy-back."

"How would you do it?" Herm asks.

"Why, simply by carrying a second type of sign. Something like FREE ENTERPRISE WORKS. Or SUPPORT PEOPLE'S CAPITALISM. See what I mean? The potential would be tremendous. Tremendous."

"But," Herm objected, "what would that sort of an added emphasis do to the blimp's primary purpose? After all, the whole idea was a religious one. Now if we change that—"

"No need to change, Herm. Just add the other one on. As to what it will do to the religious impact, I have a hunch that it would increase it. Increase it. The new emphasis would bring a certain stability by tying your religious message into life today. That's my hunch, and my hunches have built up D.-S. Advertising to a fifty million gross."

"I'm afraid it wouldn't work," Herm disagreed. "If for no other reason, we're dependent on a whole lot of religious people all over the country to support the

Gospel Blimp. Costs close to eight thousand dollars a month. Monkey with the blimp's purpose and that income could dry up overnight. It's hard enough getting money anyway today, without turning your supporters against you. No, I'm afraid the idea's out.—Not that I don't think it's a good one, Mr. Sanders. I can see where the genius for your company's campaigns have come from. I'm not against the idea—it's brilliant."

"Ever think of new sources of income, Herm?" the National Steel treasurer asks.

"I dream about them every night!" Herm laughs. "But few of my dreams materialize."

"Ever think of tapping the big corporations? Of getting money from some of the leaders in industry who aren't particularly religious?"

Herm shook his head. "They'd never get interested in the Gospel Blimp."

"Probably not. But they might get very much interested in this new idea. I'm pretty sure my company would. And we're just one of many. Think it over, Herm. That's my advice. Take it up with your board. If they're big men they'll not miss an opportunity like this. Neither will you. It could mean a great deal to you personally."

"Thank you, Sir. I'll certainly bring it up to my board."

AND BRING IT UP he did, at the next board meeting.

It was on Friday night. Everybody was out, because
Herm had passed the word around that something important was going to be presented. At Herm's request
the public relations fellow also was invited to sit in on
the meeting.

Usually our board meetings were rather routine,
mostly approving budgets and other business which
Herm presented. For one thing, none of us had the
time to put in on these things that Herm had, and so
we just figured we had to have confidence in his recom-
mendations.

Herm took devotions at the beginning of the meeting
this particular night. He strung together a lot of different Bible passages, starting with the one about being
wise as serpents and harmless as doves. Then he read
a couple of parables—one about the men who were
given the talents to invest, another about the tares grow-
ing among the wheat. He ended up with several verses
about prayer being answered. Then he called on the
public relations fellow to pray. (Usually we had a
round of prayer, but not tonight.)

After we've disposed of a few other items of business, Herm says he has something new to present—
something we may even be opposed to initially. But he
wants us to listen with open heads before we come
to any decision. And he'd like not to be interrupted
with questions until he's given us the whole picture.

So he begins by giving a sort of summary of everything that's happened since that first summer night in
George and Ethel's backyard (only he doesn't name

them). He goes through all the developments, all the problems we've licked, all the things we've accomplished.

"If we're realistic," he says, "we've done a fair job of evangelizing our city. Maybe not perfect, but nothing human's perfect. At any rate, everybody's seen the Gospel Blimp. It's been a great testimony. Great.

"Now we've come to a possible major break-through. Up to this point we've been a rather small operation. Oh, I know it's seemed big—backbreaking at times. But is this our horizon? Have we reached the summit of Everest? Or is there more land to be possessed? I think there is. I think the past up to this moment is only introductory, that a step of faith at this point— well, I think you'll agree with me after I've told you what I have to propose."

So he tells us about what happened last week on the golf course, about Mr. Sanders' suggestion. Then he ends by giving us his opinion, which is that we ought to go along with the idea.

"I know that some people, perhaps even some of you fellows on the board, will think this is compromise, that we ought to continue to be just what we've always been. But you've got to be realistic. If we're going to advance, if we're going to forge ahead, why I think there's only one way. At least it's the only way I've heard up to the present time. Any of you fellows have anything else to suggest, why I'll be glad to listen. Floor's open for discussion. Or a motion."

Several of us jump in at the same time.

One says that he feels when God has raised up something like the Gospel Blimp, we ought to be awful careful about changing it.

Herm replies that there is no question about a change. There would be no change in the ministry of the blimp. Absolutely no change. This would only mean that a new emphasis would be added.

But, another asks, wouldn't it mean less hours for the gospel signs? How can you have both without the gospel being affected?

Maybe, Herm suggests, we could combine the two types of sign. He's just thinking off the top of his head, he says, but it does seem like a distinct possibility.

We went on like that for a couple of hours, nobody really satisfied with Herm's plans for the blimp. Nobody, that is, except the public relations fellow. He sided with Herm on every point.

Finally it came to a vote, or at least it would have come to that. But Herm saw which way the wind was blowing, so he suggested that instead of voting tonight, we appoint a committee to meet with Mr. Sanders and a few other men, business executives. Then the committee could report back and we'd be in a position to decide at our next meeting.

That sounded reasonable, so we tabled the matter and Herm appointed himself and two other board members, plus the public relations fellow, to the committee. Soon afterward we broke up for the night.

10

Those Worldly Griscoms

O N THE WAY home I passed by George Griscom's house. I hadn't seen him for weeks, and I didn't want him to think our friendship had been affected by his dropping off the blimp. So I decided to stop, even though it was getting a bit late.

Their place was sort of dark, only one light on downstairs. In a few minutes Ethel came to the door, her hair half up in curlers.

"Come on in," she says. "It's certainly been a long time since we've seen you. George will be sorry he missed you."

"George away?" I ask. "I shouldn't really have stopped, it's so late. But you know how it is. I'm on my way home from the blimp board meeting, and I thought I'd just stop by to say hello."

"I'm certainly glad you did. We were talking about you and your family just the other day. George was saying we'd have to have you over for a lasagna supper or something. Yes, George is away until Sunday afternoon. He went to the shore with the man next door. You know, the one everybody's been praying for so long. He's got a small boat and they'll be doing some fishing out in the bay. Maybe the ocean too, not far out. But George hopes it'll just be the bay," she ends with a little laugh. "He gets deathly sick in any sort of rough water. He turns positively green. You should see him."

"No, I won't come in tonight. It's too late, and besides I mainly wanted to see George. Thought I'd bring him up-to-date on the Gospel Blimp.—This guy next door, has he become a Christian?"

"Not yet. But we're praying for him."

"So are we. And the Commander's not forgetting either."

"I know. The blimp comes over the neighborhood pretty often. And the bombs really clutter—I mean, there are a lot of them dropped. Just the other day George was mentioning it while he was cleaning out the downspout."

"Well, I'd better be getting home. Tomorrow I've got to do some painting and cleaning around the hangar. It's a full day's work, so I want to start early. So I'd better be getting home and to bed. Tell George I stopped, and tell him"—here I sort of laughed—"tell him I hope he's not falling into bad company since he got off the blimp board. What I mean is, we'd love to have him back. And you know how it is when you get away from Christian fellowship and with a beer-drinking, card-playing crowd. Not that I want to mind George's business, but you know how it is. But we'll be praying."

"Thanks. George'll be glad you stopped." She seemed

to hesitate, then she said it real fast, so fast I almost missed it as I started down off the porch. "It's easy to get out of the world on a blimp, isn't it?"

Out of the world on a blimp. I thought about it all the way home, but I couldn't quite figure out what she meant. Oh well. Ethel is probably just browned off about the blimp going so well and their not being involved in it any longer. I sure hope George hasn't started to drink or smoke. He's such a nice guy—it would be a shame to see him go down the river. But like they say, birds of a feather. I'll have to bring it up for prayer, I decide, at the blimp prayer meeting Sunday afternoon. And the women will have to remember Ethel, too. Her not seeming worried about George. That's something. Wonder if they ever were really one with us.

At any rate, I'm glad he's no longer on the board. It'd just take one guy who doesn't believe in the separated life to put the blimp on the skids. Really on the skids. But so far the Lord's been good to us. Taking George off, and keeping us from a split. Really good.

11

Some Bright New Signs

A FEW WEEKS later the blimp started to carry the new type of signs. They were beautifully designed (D.-S. Advertising had done them) and for the first few days, until we got fresh gospel signs, there was quite a contrast.

The gospel ones had been out in all sorts of weather for over two years now. So they were sort of shabby and worn. You never realized it, though, until the new type were used.

Besides, there were a few changes that had to be made in the gospel signs when the new emphasis was added. For instance, as Mr. Sanders pointed out to the board, it was sort of funny coupling ALL HAVE SINNED and FREE ENTERPRISE THE PERFECT SYSTEM together. They were, in his words, sort of incompatible. Same way with I AM THE WAY and MY WAY'S THE AMERICAN WAY.

Since I was one of those on the board who questioned this new approach when Herm first brought it up, I suppose I ought to tell you that it really seemed to go over. For one thing, the fellows in the office where

I work gradually seemed to change in their attitude toward the blimp. They now had sort of a respect for it, and you could have knocked me over with a feather when one day the boss called me into his office and gave me a check for I.G.B.I.

Of course the guys outside in the plant weren't too favorable toward the blimp, especially after the new emphasis was added. They'd make cracks whenever I had to go out there from the office for something. Cracks like "The blimp's wearing a white collar now," and "Blimps and bosses are full of hot air."

These women on the sub-assembly line also really began to rib me. One of them would scream, "Save me, save me," whenever I poked my head in the door.

"I will save you," someone across the room shouts back.

"Who are you to save me?" the first girl yells.

"I'm the president of National Steel," she answers. "Come unto me and rust." Then they all go into gales of laughter.

Ignorant people. Members of unions. It's that sort of people don't appreciate the free enterprise system. Blasphemous, almost, the way they'll pervert Scripture to their own ends sometimes. Like I just quoted, "Come unto me and rust." But then, they don't know the Lord, so you can understand, sort of, their mixing Scripture up with their prejudices.

Financially God was pouring out his blessing upon the blimp. Some donors fell off, and we got a few letters disagreeing with the new emphasis. But in the main Christian people stood with us, especially after we told them of the way these other Christians were disagreeing with us on the change. That seemed to make the Lord's people rally round the blimp, I guess to make up for the break in the ranks.

But the big financial boost came from all these important men and corporations and foundations. Only way I can explain it is a miracle, a miracle by which God worked in their hearts.

And we also got a whole lot of good advice and practical help as a result of the change. Herm saw to it that the board was enlarged so these big men could be included on it. One of the top lawyers in the city took care of changing the constitution, and he didn't even have to go to the state capital. When I think of all we went through to get that constitution and the charter in the first place, it really seems wonderful we could get the change made so easily.

Everything was sort of like that. Expert advice, the very best that was available, on every question. When the next year's budget was discussed, the treasurer of National Steel had all sorts of charts prepared to show projected donations, business trends and other factors, on the basis of which we could determine our rate of expansion.

I guess our choice of verses to carry on the blimp must have been pretty hit-or-miss before the new emphasis. About all we did was pray about it. But when these new men got on the board, after its reorganization, especially Mr. Sanders, we sure weren't walking around in the dark any longer. His agency did marketing research on slogans and came up with answers in black and white. I tell you, he sure knew what he was doing. And he could make it all so plain to us through visual presentations.

Like I said, God really honored this new step of faith. It almost made you ashamed when you thought of how we floundered around in the early days of the blimp.

FROM THEN ON the Gospel Blimp was really organized. You could feel it in every part of the work, from the spacious new offices with their modern furniture and illuminated map of the city to the regular maintenance program on the blimp.

At long last we were in good with all, or almost all, the Protestant ministers in the city. Each Saturday we advertised a different church on the blimp. If any Sunday school had a contest, the winner was given a blimp ride. Most churches even had a special "Blimp Stewardship Sunday." We provided free church bulletins, with a photo of the blimp against a blue sky and a church steeple and an American flag on the front, and a low-key writeup about the blimp on the back. As a result, more and more churches put us on their budget.

Same way with the city itself. Everyone was speaking well of us. This was partly due, I'm sure, to the caliber of new men who were on the I.G.B.I. board. But we were also doing little things to show our responsible community relations, things like running a sign on the blimp, DON'T FORGET TO VOTE, on election day, taking part in parades, and other things like that.

Things had been going that way for several months, and it just made you thankful, also sort of proud, that you'd had a part in the original blimp vision. We often spoke of it at board meetings.

IT HARDLY SEEMED POSSIBLE that almost three years had passed since the idea first occurred to us. So one night I was surprised to get a phone call from George Griscom.

"Know what next Friday is?" George asks, after we've said hello, and how are you, and all the rest.

"Next Friday? No, can't say I do. Some sort of holiday?"

"No," he replies. "Something happened next Friday three years ago. Remember—you were over at our house for a picnic supper."

"Wait," I interrupt. "Now I know. That was the night we had our idea for the Gospel Blimp. A lot's happened since then."

"Sure has. Ethel and I were just talking, and we got to wondering if it wouldn't be a nice idea to invite everybody over next Friday who was here that night three years ago. Sort of a celebration, auld lang syne and all that."

"Sounds like a wonderful idea. I'm glad that you're still, well, I mean—"

"Still interested in I.G.B.I. and the blimp? Sure we are, though we haven't had much time to spend on it. And of course you know we haven't agreed with everything that's gone on. But Friday night we won't have to go into all that. We can just have a picnic supper and remember the good old days."

"Well, count on us. I don't know about the rest, but we'll certainly be there. Anything we can bring— potato salad or ham or anything?"

"No just your appetite," George says with a laugh. "Ethel will take care of everything."

I asked around and found that everyone had the same sort of phone call and invitation from George, only I didn't find out about Marge. And they all planned to be there except Herm. It seems he had a previous engagement.

12

Fulfillment

FRIDAY NIGHT came, a beautiful summer evening. We were the first ones there, and we found George in the yard, trying to hurry a charcoal fire along. "Welcome," he says. "You're just in time to help me get this fire going. Also to meet my friend and next-door neighbor."

This fellow I didn't know, but recognized, was standing up by this time, having been kneeling next to the grill and blowing into it.

I was surprised, but I didn't say anything about it, even after I was alone with George. (The neighbor went into the house with my wife, to help Ethel bring some things outside. I found out later that his wife was there too.)

Seemed sort of funny to introduce somebody like this to the group. And I was sure that even if I was quiet about it, everybody else wouldn't be. Before the evening was over somebody was sure to say something to George and Ethel.

Especially since the neighbor was smoking. I hasten to add that smoke doesn't particularly bother me, but

there are some that it does. And even though it wasn't
so bad out in the yard as it would have been indoors,
there were some who would certainly not appreciate
the introduction of this worldly element to our Christian circle.

As different people came, you could tell they were
surprised and a little put out to find the next-door
neighbors there. And smoking. It just sort of took the
edge off the celebration. Not that anyone said anything
to the neighbors—we were all nice enough to them. It
was more the little remarks people made to each other.
George and Ethel couldn't help seeing our reaction.

I must say that Ethel pulled out all the stops on that
supper. She had everything, ending with ice-cold water-
melon, the first of the season.

George had just collected the rinds in a bucket, and
we were all sitting around on deck chairs and folding
chairs. Somebody tried to strike up "I'm so happy, and
here's the reason why," but everybody was too full to
be much interested in singing. So she gave up after a
few lines.

At this point George sets the bucket down and begins to talk to the group. He recalls how we were all
here three years ago, and how it was a night just like
tonight. Even an airplane going over like is going over
just now.

We all look up at the twinkling lights.

"That night," George says, "we had the idea of a
Gospel Blimp for the first time. And that's the reason
we're celebrating tonight—what brings us together.

But that's not all. If you remember, the thing that got us thinking about evangelizing the city that night was my next-door neighbors. They were sitting on the porch, if you'll recall.

"And during the past three years there's been a lot of prayer that these neighbors would become Christians, that they'd put their trust in Jesus Christ.

"Tonight I invited them over to have supper with the group because—well, to cut it short, God has answered our praying. They've become Christians."

Well, you should have heard the group when George told us that. We were really excited. Everybody wanted to ask questions at the same time.

"Was it a verse on the blimp or a fire bomb?"

"Day or night? I mean, was the verse in electric lights?"

"It must have been while we were still using the P.A. system. Do you remember what Herm said in his message?"

"Did you both accept the same invitation—I mean, at the same time the invitation was given over the P.A. system?"

"What tract was in the fire bomb? And did you fill in decision cards?"

"Hey," George says, loud enough to be heard. "Hey, give them a break. One question at a time. And don't jump to any conclusions. Let them tell you."

So we finally quiet down, and the next-door neighbor begins to speak.

"Like George told you, we're Christians now. Both of us. But it wasn't the blimp."

"It wasn't?"

"You mean the blimp didn't save you, the Lord saved you? That what you mean?"

"No, I mean God didn't use the blimp. Fact of the matter is, the blimp irritated me, to put it mildly. Always cruising over our place and bothering us with that P.A. system, and dropping trash—that's what I considered it then—dropping trash on our lawn and in the rain gutters."

"But we were praying you'd be saved through the blimp."

"Sure, and God answered. But not by the blimp."

"But by people connected with the blimp."

"Well, not exactly. At least not while they were spending all their time on the blimp. I mean George and Ethel. We've already told them, so I can tell you that we thought they were lousy neighbors."

"Lousy neighbors? But they were awfully concerned for your soul's salvation. You should have heard them pray for you at the regular prayer meetings."

"I did. It was once when the women met over here and I was working out in my yard. I heard Ethel pray for us, that we'd be saved. But they were still lousy neighbors. Always busy working on blimp business, never any time for us. We'd invite them over for an evening, or have tickets for the ice hockey game. Once it was the garden show. But no matter what it was, they didn't have time for us. They only seemed to have time for the blimp."

"Remember that night we were going over accounts and he stopped by?" George asks, turning to me. "That night he invited Ethel and me to go to the shore. But I turned him down—blimp meetings Saturday and Sunday. That's the way we were."

"Sorry, George. I didn't mean to make it so strong," the next-door neighbor says. "It's just that—"

"No," George interrupts, "don't back down on what you said. That's the way we were. Stinking neighbors, Ethel and me. But we're glad you're not just neighbors now, but friends. And a brother and sister in Christ. That's what counts. Really counts. —Well, folks, guess maybe we'd better think about breaking up. We don't want to keep you too long. We did promise some of you we'd break up early."

"Wait a minute, George," the neighbor says. "I haven't told the people how we became Christians."

"Sure you have." You can tell George wants it to end there.

"Let him go on, George," I say. "It's not too late, and besides, anybody with a babysitter who has to get home can leave. Let's hear the rest. We've got plenty of time."

"It won't take more than a few minutes to tell you the rest," the next-door neighbor says. "I don't want to keep you. But the last thing in the world I'd want you to leave thinking is that we're criticizing George and Ethel. Why, they've been Christ Himself to us ever since that second time the wife went into the hospital."

"Ethel came to see me every day," his wife explained. "I was so terribly discouraged that I had to go back in. But Ethel would visit me, and bring some flowers from her garden and just sit and talk. She was always so cheery and understanding. She'd read to me, and she'd talk about Jesus Christ. I'd never met anyone before to whom He was real. It seems strange, but I never had."

"I was awfully low, too," said her husband. "But George and Ethel had me over there for supper every night. And after supper George would read the Bible and pray at the table. He didn't read a lot, but what he read made sense. And I was struck with the same thing that struck the wife: Jesus was real to these people. They weren't putting on a show for our benefit.

"Like just before the wife came home from the hospital. Any of you guys ever spend two weeks keeping house with the wife away? You know what I mean—everything all crudded up. Not just egg stuck to the plates—egg stuck to the egg which is stuck to the plates. Bed linens, towels. You know how it is. Well, Ethel came in the day before and gave that house the going-over of its life."

"Yes," his wife added, "and for a month after I got home she wouldn't let me do a stitch of washing or ironing. Took all our dirty clothes home and did them."

"That's about it," the next-door neighbor finished. "We could tell you more—like George going to the shore Saturdays to fish with me, even when he knew I had beer in the cooler. Sure, I knew how you felt about drinking, George—but you weren't a Holy Joe about it. If you had been I'd probably never have been interested in doing anything with you. And we'd probably not have become Christians."

There is silence. Everyone's thinking.

"Well," I finally say, "that was interesting. But I've got a big day tomorrow—I'm planting some perennials out at the entrance to the hangar. So I guess I'd better call it a night. Yes, it's been quite a night. Always wonderful to find out that God has answered prayer. He never fails, does He?"

"Sure doesn't," someone agrees. "Maybe not the answer we thought, but He always answers."

A sudden thought strikes me. "Hey," I say to the next-door neighbor, "how about coming out to the hangar with me tomorrow and working on the blimp? You'd enjoy it."

"Sorry," he says. "George and I are going bowling with the guy across the street."

13

An Interpretation

THE LITTLE CITY where the Gospel Blimp was conceived is the world, our latter twentieth century American world, in which Christians work and play, raise children, buy automobiles and face the devil.

The Christians are you and I, and believers we know. In the main, we're sincere people, knowing that it's God's will for the gospel to be presented to every person, and trying as best we know how to obey that will.

George and Ethel Griscom's next door neighbors are the people who live next door to you and me (or in the apartment above, or down the road, or on the next quarter-section). Not that our neighbors all drink beer and play cards on the porch of a summer evening. No, they may attend symphony concerts and lead the local W.C.T.U. Some of them may even sit near us on Sunday morning.

But whether they like gardening or poker, whether they stopped school at eighth grade or teach in the university, whether they are wonderful neighbors or the high fence kind, these people have one thing in common with the Griscoms' neighbors: they haven't yet received the Lord Jesus Christ. They need Him desperately, although they may seldom think about Him. And we know, when we think about these neighbors, that we're responsible to God for a Christian witness to them.

Of course, that witness is the eternal gospel, the wonderfully good news that "Christ died for our sins according to the Scriptures, and that He was buried, and that He rose again the third day according to the Scriptures" (I Corinthians 15:3, 4). We know, all of us believers, that there is only one saving message, and that only through personal faith in the Lord Jesus Christ can anyone be justified before God.

And the blimp? Why the wonderful Gospel Blimp is every impersonal, external means by which we try to fulfil our responsibility to witness to our neighbors. Gospel programs over the radio, messages on billboards or in tracts: these are some of our blimps. They either supplement our own personal witness or else they're substitutes for involvement with our neighbors —the sort of involvement that George and Ethel discovered toward the end of the story.

But still, there is a measure of involvement, even in these things. There's the involvement of paying for the billboard signs and radio time, of giving out the tracts and maintaining all our gospel projects. But these are poor substitutes for personal communication of the gospel, the sort of witnessing we glimpse from afar in the New Testament.

Today we have perfected various technical means of

presenting the Christian message. We are hitting a
mass market with mass gospel media. But in the proc-
ess, we have often passed our personal responsibility
on to blimps and loud speakers and impersonal organizations.

But technical, organizational means have one enor-
mous lack: a human heart. They may multiply a voice
ten thousand times, but it remains only a voice.

The great period of Christian witness was the half
century after Pentecost, A.D. 30. Those were the days
when kings and slaves—and priests—heard about Jesus
Christ from living witnesses. So did a lot of ordinary
people. During that generation every part of the Ro-
man Empire was penetrated, and places as distant as
India were even reached according to tradition. This
occurred during a period of technical barrenness, for
Christians then had none of our modern means for
spreading the gospel. The printing press was not yet
invented, radio and television were twenty centuries
distant—but those were the days when Christians shook
the world.

Jesus Christ didn't commit the gospel to an advertising agency; He commissioned disciples. And He
didn't command them to put up signs and pass out
tracts; He said that they would be His witnesses.

Those first disciples were lights set on the twin lamp-
stands of Christian morality and Christian love, shining
in the darkness of a hostile pagan culture, or the twi-
light of a hostile religious culture, which was more
difficult.

No message in the sky could match the witness of their holy lives and works of love. "Let your light so shine before men," their Lord commanded, "that they may see your good works and glorify your Father which is in heaven" (Matthew 5:16).

And they did.

The public preaching and private witnessing of those first generation Christians were illuminated by the light of their Christian conduct.

When the light was bright, the preaching was powerful. When the light became dim, the world passed up the preaching. And the Lord moved to extinguish both light and preaching, for no dim and dying light could draw men to the Light of the World. Then or now.

Therefore the great emphasis of New Testament teaching (both in the Gospels and in the Epistles) was not upon means of telling the Christian gospel, but upon the necessity of living the Christian life. Jesus Christ never taught His disciples how to preach; He only taught them how to pray and how to live.

And in the Epistles, the great enemy which threatens the life of the Church is not external persecution. The enemy is within: immorality and doctrinal heresy. Against these Church discipline is enjoined.

Slaves, said the Apostle Paul to Titus, should "adorn the doctrine of God our Savior" by obeying their masters, by going several steps further and pleasing them in all things, not answering back, not stealing, but rendering faithful service. Here is no suggestion that the slaves should scrawl texts on the sides of Cretan galleys.

Those slaves *were* the texts, illuminated ones. And so were Christian masters, and husbands, wives, children, older people and pastors. Or at least they were commanded to be.

But are American Christians short on personal morality? If by morality we mean "the separated life," our answer is no. In the general understanding of the term, we are recognized as living up to a half-dozen don'ts.

But if we mean our Lord's high standard in the Sermon on the Mount, and the moral-ethical teachings of the Epistles, the answer is surely yes. Our adherence to a clearly defined pattern of conduct ("the separated life") may in itself be a moral short cut, involving "tithes of mint and anise and cummin," while we omit the "weightier matters of the law" (Matthew 23:23).

The time is long overdue for a change in moral and ethical emphasis from what we don't do to what we do and what we are.

"By this shall all men know that ye are my disciples," said the Lord Jesus, "if ye have love one to another." And He defined love in terms of visiting the sick, feeding the hungry, clothing the shabby, encouraging the imprisoned. The Apostle added visiting widows and orphans to His list, and also said that we should comfort the sorrowful, strengthen the afflicted, and restore the morally defeated.

Our blimps reflect us, but our love reflects Christ.

One problem all Christians face is our increasing

isolation from the world, from neighbors and associates who are not Christians. By monopolizing our time, most of our Christian activities only increase our distance from others, even activities like International Gospel Blimps, Inc., that exist for an evangelistic purpose. We attend committee meetings, we serve on boards, we prepare dinners, we run the mimeograph, we organize and reorganize.

And we end up without time to get to know our neighbors, let alone to love them. For love is doing, not feeling. Therefore love demands time.

Besides, it's so much more pleasant to sit in our little Christian groups and plan how the Gospel Blimp will evangelize our neighbors than it is to do the evangelizing ourselves. There are no embarrassing problems at Christian committee meetings, such as the offer of a cocktail or a language slip. There is no discussion of an article which appeared in the *Atlantic* (or some other magazine with which we're unfamiliar), no disturbing viewpoint about the strike at the finishing plant, no off-color jokes with which to cope, no question about why God (if He really exists) is letting poor old Mrs. Hanson down the street suffer so with cancer. And of course there are no afternoons spent sitting with Mrs. Hanson or washing her bed linens.

Then when the day comes for us to float our blimps or hold our meetings, we wonder why our neighbors seem totally uninterested, unaffected.

Small wonder. We share an advertisement of the gospel with them instead of sharing Christ. We de-

mand that they bridge the gap to us, instead of ac-
cepting our responsibility to construct bridges of love
and understanding to them.

"Go ye," said our Lord, not "Get them to come."

Now how about Herm?

Herm is both villain and victim, a man who, having
put his hand to the plow, turns back—not leaving
Christian work, which would be far better, but re-
maining in it, placing his stamp upon it, taking pos-
session of it, damaging it, destroying it.

The work takes the place of God (if God ever did
have a place), and then the man takes the place of the
work.

Who among God's servants does not fear lest he
might be Herm, not ending well, a castaway after
preaching to others. "Lord, is it I?"

But Herm is also a victim. Christians might well
pray more for our contemporary leaders and adulate
them less. The man who attains a position of leader-
ship tends to be increasingly insulated from criticism.

Such criticism should properly come from the board
of directors, which is legally and morally responsible
for the work. But too often board members abandon
their authority, simply approving what the leader does.
If internal or external problems arise, their tendency
is to defend the leader, instead of subjecting him and
the work to Biblical standards of judgment. Whether
this attitude arises out of a sense of loyalty (since in
most instances the leader is responsible for the suggestion of men to be elected to the board), or out of

a desire to "keep the work from suffering," there is little difference in the result, which is spiritual erosion of both leader and work.

Unfortunately, many Christians who are faithful in praying for a man on his way up consider him beyond the need of prayer—or at least their humble praying—after he attains a position of prominence. Yet then his need is greater, both because he is influencing more people, and also because he is now more vulnerable to various temptations, especially pride.

One great factor in pride is our American demand for bigness. We must increase the budget, employ more workers, nationalize (better yet, internationalize) the scope of our activities, acquire more property, take over more elaborate physical facilities: these are our Christian status symbols. And not merely status on a human level, for divine status as well is proved by these signs of outward prosperity. Financial provision for an enlarging program is usually considered the prime evidence that a Christian work is proceeding according to the will of God.

But this may not be so. Other factors beside God, or instead of God, can produce plentiful money. Anticommunism is such a factor. So is a defense of the American system. Cleverly handled, such causes can open checkbooks snapped shut against the gospel alone. So can the advocacy of various other political, social and economic viewpoints.

But adding anything to the gospel of Christ must weaken it. Jesus Christ refused to fall into this trap.

"My kingdom," He said, "is not of this world." And as if to emphasize the point, He chose disciples of the most diverse political opinions: Matthew, the collaborator with Rome, and Simon, member of the Canaanite resistance movement against Rome.

I do not suggest that any area of contemporary life should be excluded from Biblical insights and prophetic preaching. But areas of proper concern for Christians within the Church are not our message to the world outside.

We preach Christ, not the capitalistic system. We seek to bring our neighbors to faith in Him, not to our opinion about free enterprise. To tie Jesus Christ to the very best human system is to tie a star, light years distant, to a dead horse here on earth. Neither star nor Christ will thus be bound.

Further, our unsaved neighbors include those who do not hold our political, economic and social opinions. We may not care for the opinions they hold, but Jesus Christ died for socialists as well as capitalists, for members of A.F.L.-C.I.O. as well as members of N.A.M., for Negroes as well as whites. Shall we interpose our opinions between the Lord Jesus Christ and men for whom He died?

"If our gospel be hid in America today" (to paraphrase II Corinthians 4:3-7), "it is hid to Negroes and other minority groups, to members of labor unions, to the unchurched, the poor, the unwanted.

"Now we know that the god of this world has blinded their minds, lest the light of the glorious gospel of Christ, who is the image of God, should shine in their hearts.

"But in view of this, we should be all the more careful not to preach ourselves, or our opinions, but Christ Jesus the Lord. As for ourselves, we should be mere servants, showing love to our neighbors for Jesus' sake.

"And when we fall short in our witness (as we surely will), when our love weakens, what then? Then we know afresh that we have this treasure in earthen vessels, that the excellency of the power may be of God and not of us."

Therefore let us trust the Sovereign God, not our human organizations or institutions. And let us seek to be men and women like the Lord Jesus Christ, friends of publicans and sinners, yet "holy, harmless, undefiled, separate from sinners" (Hebrews 7:26).

And if He dashes our proud blimps to earth, we know this, that He designs thereby to bring sons to glory.